It's another Quality Book from CGP

This book has been carefully written for Year 3 children learning science. It's full of questions and investigations designed to cover the Year 3 objectives on 'Animals, including humans' from the latest National Curriculum.

There's also plenty of practice at 'Working Scientifically' throughout the book.

What CGP is all about

Our sole aim here at CGP is to produce the highest quality books — carefully written, immaculately presented and dangerously close to being funny.

Then we work our socks off to get them out to you — at the cheapest possible prices.

Contents

Section 1 — Food for Humans

Section 2 — Food for Other Animals

Section 3 — Skeletons and Muscles

Answers to the questions are on the back of the Pull-out Poster in the centre of the book.

Published by CGP

Contributors

Katie Braid, Sarah Pattison, Sean Stayte

With thanks to Jill Cousner and Sarah Williams for the proofreading.

ISBN: 978 1 78294 080 7

Clipart from Corel®

Printed by Elanders Ltd, Newcastle upon Tyne.

Based on the classic CGP style created by Richard Parsons.

Animals Need Food

Humans are a kind of animal. All animals (including humans) have to eat food. We get nutrition from the food we eat, so we need it to stay alive.

1. Look at the pictures below. Tick (✔) the boxes under food people eat.

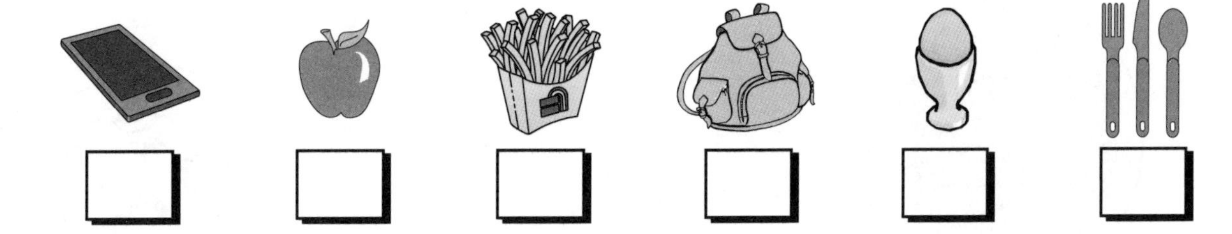

2. (Circle) the foods which **you** eat for school lunch.

Write the names of **two other** foods you eat.

1. .... 2. ....

3. Draw what you would most **like** to eat for school lunch on the plate below.

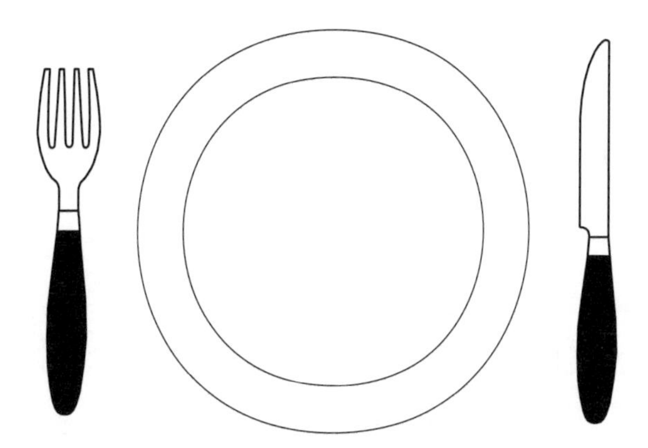

INVESTIGATE

Look at your answers for what you eat, and what you like to eat. Compare your answers with your classmates. Is there anyone who likes the same food as you do?

Food Groups

There are lots of <u>different kinds</u> of food. They can smell or taste different, and they contain different things that the body needs in order to stay <u>healthy</u>.

1. Write the **names** of the foods in the boxes below the pictures.
   The first one has been done for you.

Food Groups

2. **Similar** foods can be **grouped** together. For example, pears and oranges are both fruit. Draw all the foods from the last page in the correct food group boxes.

MEAT

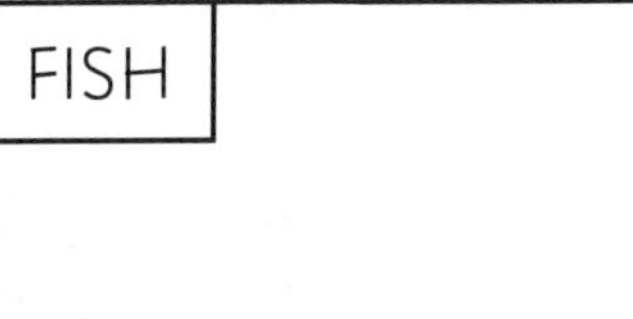

FISH

FATTY FOOD

SUGARY FOOD

STARCHY FOOD

FRUIT AND VEGETABLES

HINT: starchy foods are things like potatoes, pasta, rice and bread.

INVESTIGATE

Think of one more type of food for each category. If you can't think of anything, have a look around the cupboards and fridge at home — or in your lunchbox.

Foods for Growth

Foods like meat and fish help us grow. Pulses (lentils and beans) and eggs also help us to grow.

1. Look at the foods below and write down whether they are **meat** or **fish**.

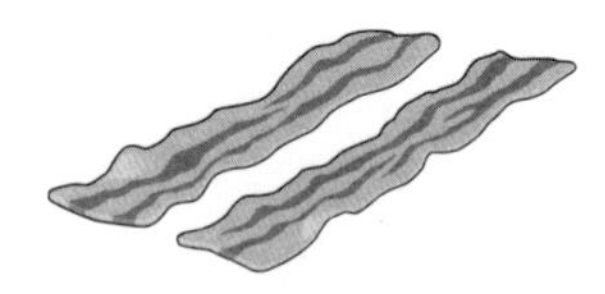

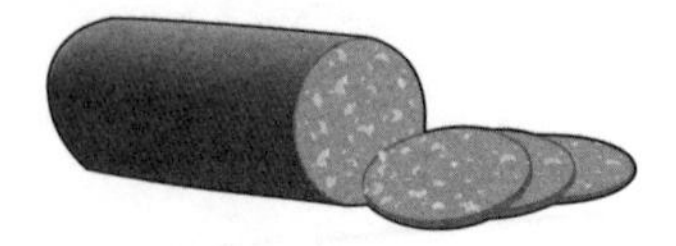

....

2. Which plate has foods on it that are better for **helping us grow**?
Put a tick (✔) in the box next to the correct plate.

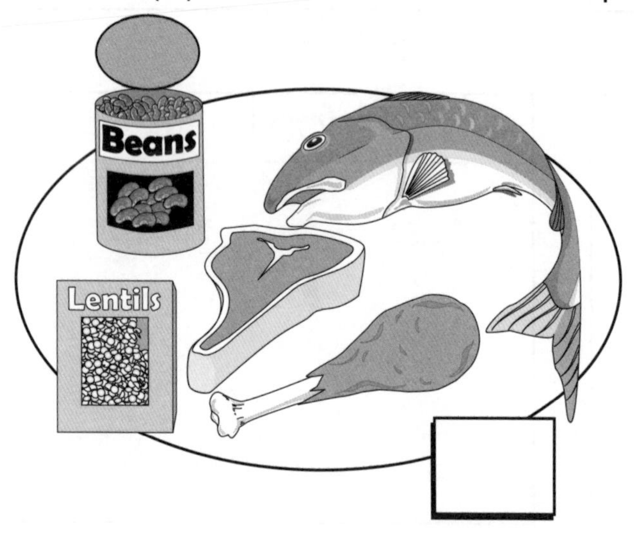

3. Look at the plate you have ticked. Write down the **names** of all the foods on it.

....

....

4. Name **two** more foods that help you grow.

1. ....

2. ....

INVESTIGATE

Keep a food diary of what you eat for breakfast, lunch and dinner for a week. At the end of the week, have a look at the diary and underline all the foods that help you to grow.

Foods for Energy

Like all animals, humans need energy for activity. We get energy from sugary and starchy foods. It's important to eat the right amount of these foods for the amount of activity you do.

1. Draw lines to show which foods are **sugary** and which are **starchy**.

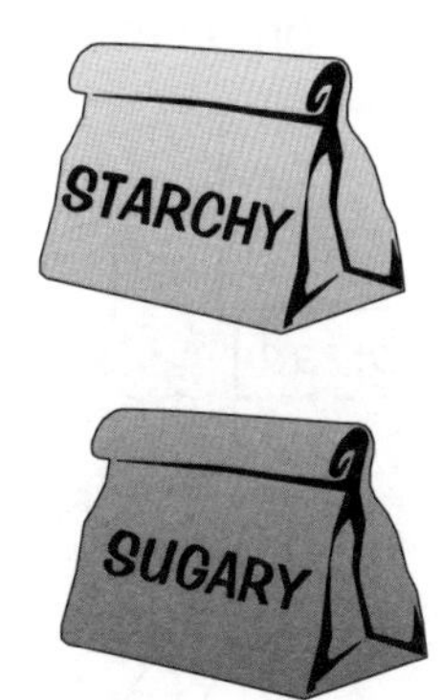

2. Use the words in the foot to complete these sentences about food.

more
exercise
moving
weight
more

Activity means .... and doing ....

People who are .... active need ....

food to keep them going. People who eat more food than they

need will put on ....

3. Dustin is going to run a big race tomorrow. He wants to eat foods that give him lots of energy. Draw rings round the **two** shopping lists that will give him the **best** foods for energy.

INVESTIGATE

Think about the activities you do in a normal day that use energy. Are there any days when you need to eat more starchy or sugary foods to give you more energy?

Balanced Diets

It's important to eat a balanced mixture of foods for energy and foods for growth. You need to make sure you eat the right amount of each type of food.

1. Each plate has a mixture of foods.
   Write '**growth**' on all the foods that help you grow.
   Write '**energy**' on all the foods that give you energy.

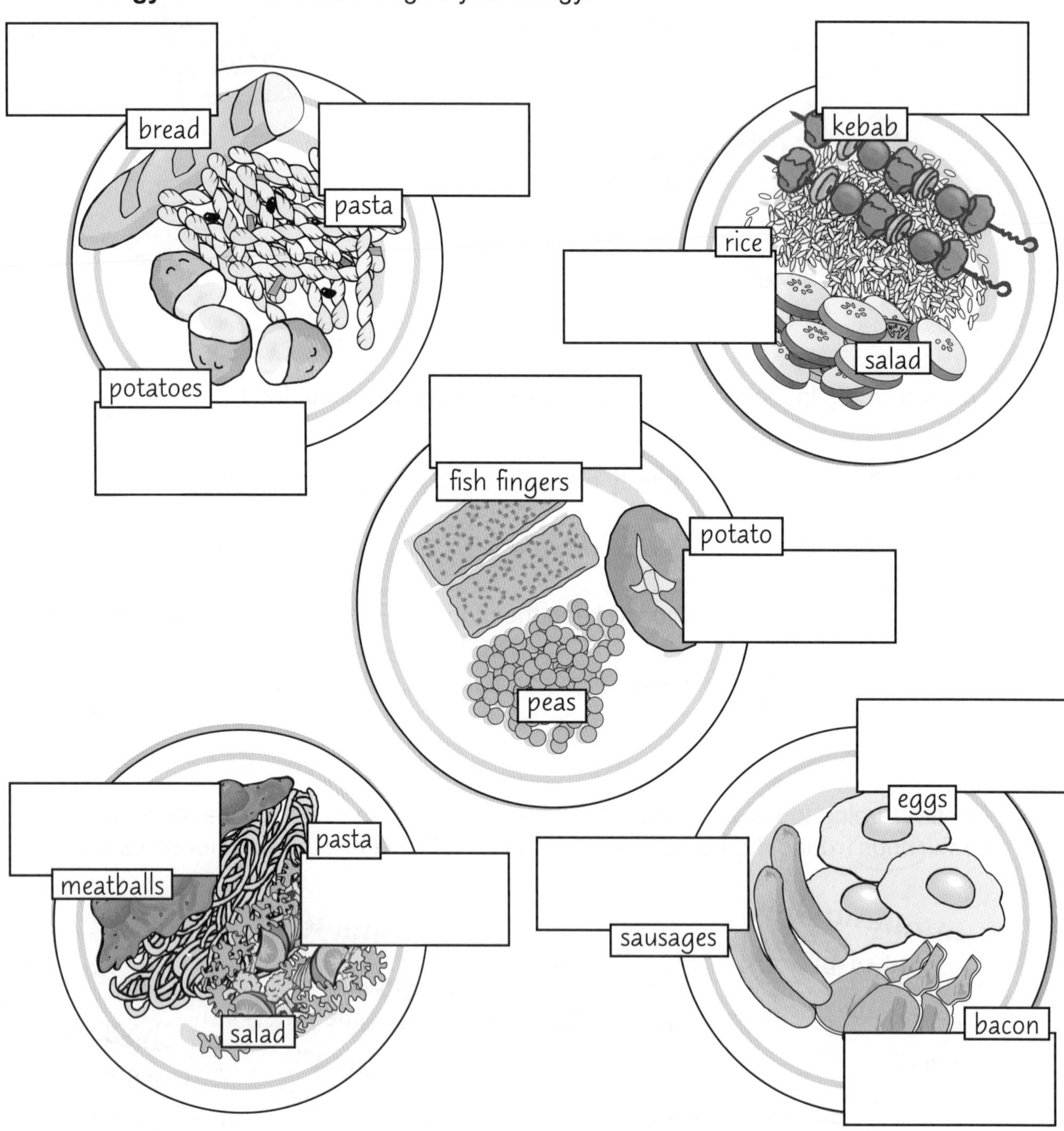

2. In a balanced meal you need **growth** foods, **energy** foods and **vegetables**.
   Tick (✔) all the meals which you think are balanced.

INVESTIGATE

Plan a balanced three-course meal (starter, main course, dessert) for a friend. Make sure you find out if they have a special diet — for example, are they vegetarian?

Animal Diets

Different animals eat different foods. Monkeys eat different food from lions... and you don't eat the same kind of food as your friend's hamster (I hope).

1. Write down what each of these pets **eats**. If you don't know the answer, ask other people in your class, or look it up in a book or on the Internet.

Some of the animals may eat more than one kind of food.

Dogs eat:

....

....

Budgerigars eat:

....

....

Goats eat:

....

....

Snakes eat:

....

....

Rabbits eat:

....

....

2. Draw a circle around all the animals above that **eat meat**.
   Draw a rectangle around all the animals that **don't eat meat**.

INVESTIGATE

Make a table with 2 columns. In the first column list some more animals. Use books or the Internet to find out what they eat and write this down in the other column. Finally, split the animals into two groups — animals that eat meat and animals that don't.

What Do Cats Eat?

In this mini-project, you'll be helping Dr. Snooze find out what to feed his new cat. He thinks that cats eat fish, but he wants to do an investigation to make sure. After that, you can have a go at your own investigation.

1. Which question should Dr. Snooze try to answer in his investigation? Circle the best question from the ones below.

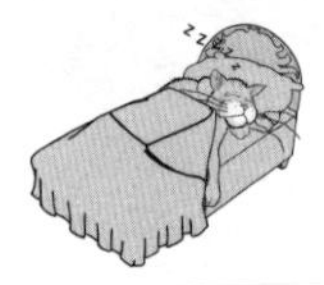
When do cats go to sleep?

Why do cats need to eat?

Do cats eat fish?

What kind of music do cats like?

2. Which **animals** should he use in the investigation? Put a tick (✔) next to the right answer.

He should use some cats and some dogs. ☐ He should use only cats. ☐ He should use one of every animal. ☐

3. How **many** cats should he use in the investigation? Put a tick (✔) next to the right answer.

Every cat in the world. ☐ Only one cat. ☐ About 5 cats. ☐

4. Circle the right words to finish off these sentences about how to do the investigation.

Dr. Snooze should (NOT / ONLY) look at cats.

He should count all different types of fish as just (FISH / FOOD) because he just wants to know if all cats eat (CHOCOLATE / FISH).

What Do Cats Eat?

5. Read the **instructions** for doing a food diary, and then fill in the **table** below. (If you can't do the investigation, use the spare results at the bottom of the page.)

1. Write the names of five people who have cats in the top row of the table.
2. Ask the cat owners what their cat ate the day before. Do this for three days.
3. Each day, if the cat ate fish then put a tick (✔) underneath its owner's name.
4. If the cat did not eat fish then put a cross (✘) in the box.

	....	....	....	....	....
Day 1					
Day 2					
Day 3					

If there are not many cat owners in the class, you could ask other people you know.

6. Fill in this tally chart, using your results from the food diary above.

You just need to draw a line for each cat in the right box. For four cats you would draw ||||, for five cats you would draw ~~||||~~

	Tally — number of cats	Total
Eats fish	....	....
Doesn't eat fish	....	....

7. Complete this bar chart using results from the tally chart.

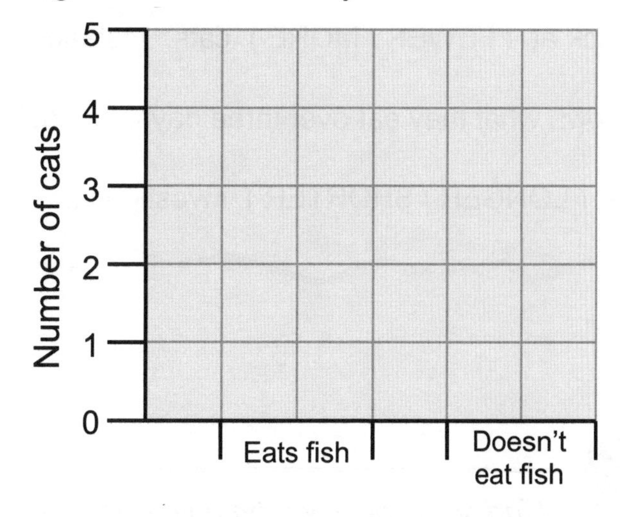

SPARE RESULTS: Tim — ate fish on Day 1. Emily — ate fish on Day 1 and Day 3. Dave — didn't eat fish. Neil — ate fish on Day 2. Ian — didn't eat fish.

What Do Cats Eat?

8. How many of the cats in your investigation ate fish? Write numbers in the spaces.

.... out of .... cats ate fish.

9. When Dr. Snooze did the investigation he found that all 5 cats ate fish, so he decided that all cats in the world eat fish. What problems might there be with the investigation?
Tick (✔) the boxes next to the two possible problems.

There were too many cats in the investigation. ☐

Fish is poisonous to cats. ☐

There were not enough cats in the investigation. ☐

The investigation was too short to be sure of the results. ☐

10. What could make the investigation better if Dr. Snooze tried to do it again?
Circle the correct words to finish off these sentences.

To make Dr. Snooze's investigation better, he could look at (FEWER / MORE) cats. Instead of writing down what they eat over three days, he could do a (LONGER / SHORTER) investigation.

EXTRA PROJECT

Find some people who own dogs and do a similar investigation. Find out how many of the dogs eat fish and compare your results with those for cats.

The Skeleton is Made of Bones

If we didn't have any bones we'd fall down in a floppy heap — we need them for support and protection. Bones of all different shapes and sizes fit together to make a skeleton.

1. Feel your own body to see where some of your bones are and try to draw them on this picture.

You can feel some of your bones in your chest — they're the hard bits. Find some of the big bones in your arms and legs and draw them too.

See what bones you can find in your fingers by feeling them. Draw some of them on this picture.

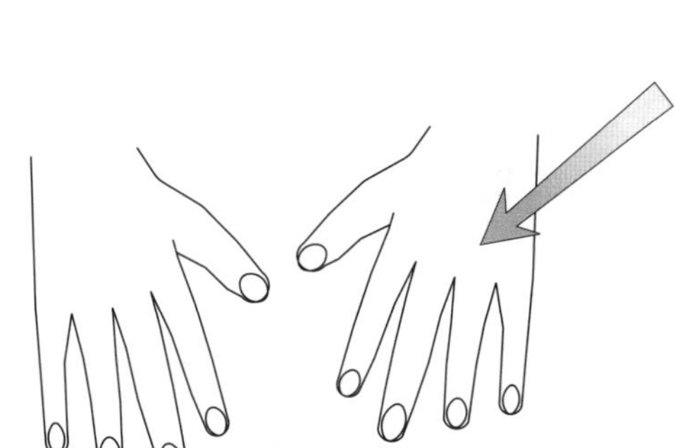

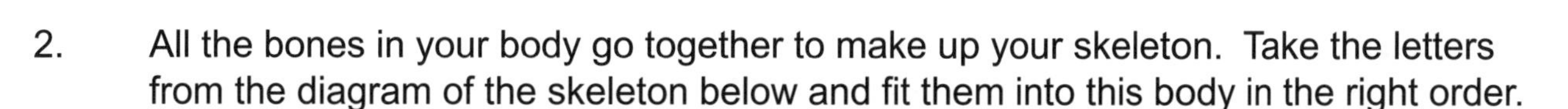

2. All the bones in your body go together to make up your skeleton. Take the letters from the diagram of the skeleton below and fit them into this body in the right order.

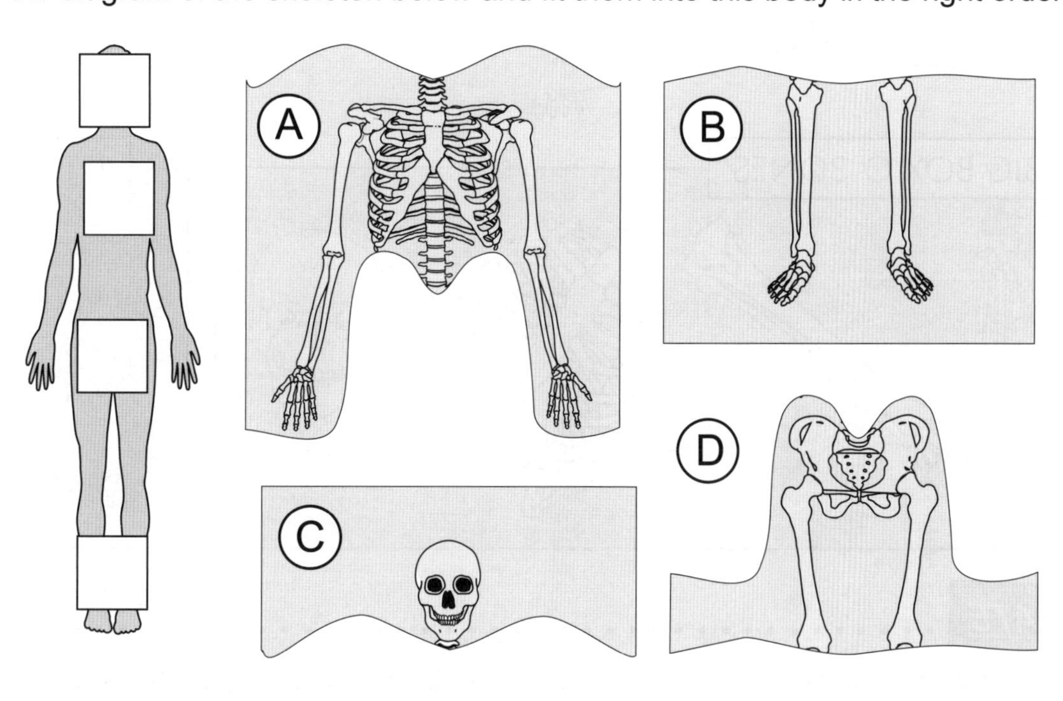

The Skeleton is Made of Bones

3. Draw the missing **pieces** onto the skeleton and fill in all the **labels**.
All the pieces and labels you need are in the boxes at the bottom of the page.

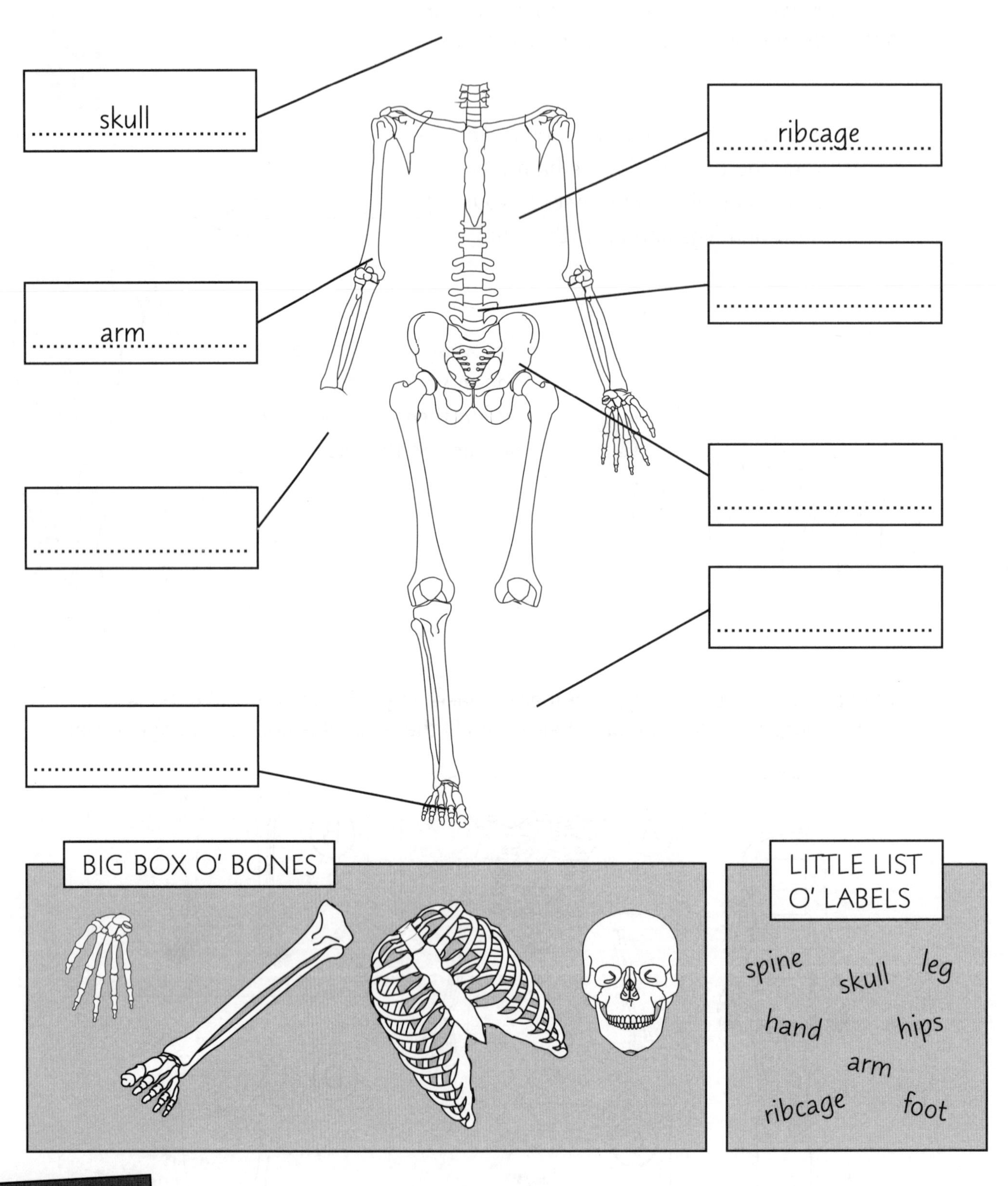

INVESTIGATE

Make a list of all the parts of your body, and write down how many different bones you can feel in each of them. Are there any parts of your body where you can't feel a bone?

Answers to Y3 'Nutrition and the Body'

7. Depends on your results. This chart uses the spare results.

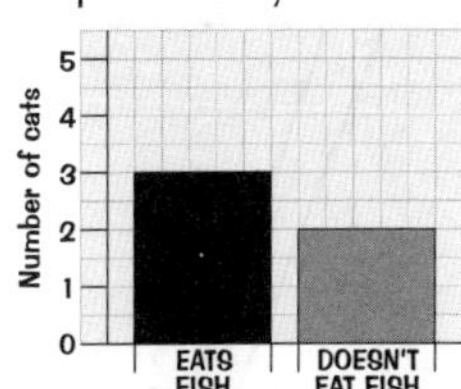

8. Depends on your results. The answer is "3 out of 5 cats ate fish" for the spare results.
9. The following should be ticked:
   There were not enough cats in the investigation.
   The investigation was too short to be sure of the results.
10. These words should be circled: more, longer.

Section 3 — Skeletons and Muscles

Pages 11-12 — The Skeleton is Made of Bones

1. The drawings should show several ribs stopping in about the right place. The arms and legs should have two bones each, with gaps or joints at the elbows and knees.
   The fingers should have three bones each. The main part of the hand should have at least five other bones.
2. From top to bottom: C, A, D, B.
3.

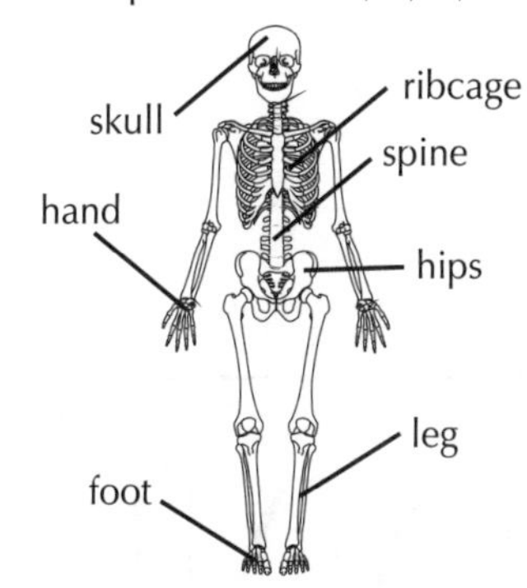

Page 13 — Animals with Skeletons

1. A — bird, B — frog, C — dog,
   D — lizard, E — human, F — fish.
2. Human yes, yes, yes, no, yes
   Dog yes, yes, no, yes, yes

Pages 14-15 — The Skeleton Supports the Body

1. Internal skeleton: goat, elephant, fish
   External skeleton: lobster, ladybird, grasshopper
   No skeleton: slug, jellyfish
2. All joints apart from the fingers and toes should be circled. (Neck, shoulders, elbows, wrists, hips, knees, ankles, tail, ears, wings.)
3. The slug, worm and squid should be circled.
4. Animals with skeletons are less flexible.

Pages 16-18 — Comparing Bone Lengths

1. Year 3 children have shorter forearms than adults.
2. B
3. Measure to and from the same points on every arm.
   Use the same ruler or tape measure for every arm you measure.
4. The numbers should be tallied in the usual way — putting a dash across to represent five.
   The frequency column should contain all numbers.
5. Any correctly drawn bar chart is OK.
6. 3, 8
7. 1. 25
   2. Depends on your results. For the spare results the most common lengths are 17 cm and 18 cm.
   3. Depends on your results (but adults should have longer forearms). For the spare results, adults had longer forearms.
8. If you ticked 'No' or 'Sort of' — did you make any mistakes when measuring? Was your test fair? Did you have enough results?

Pages 19-21 — Muscles and Bones

1. The top right arrow of both pictures should be coloured.
2. The top two sentences go with the top muscle.
   The bottom two sentences go with the bottom muscle.
3. 1. Muscle B will shorten and muscle A will lengthen.
   2. Muscle A will shorten and muscle B will lengthen.
4. bones, pairs, move, relaxes, lengthens.
5. These words should be circled: contracts, hard, relaxes.
6. The bottom muscle should be ticked.
7. It will bend even more.
8. The second box down should be ticked.
   It will get shorter.

Mixed Questions — pages 22-25

1. Fruit, meat, chocolate, grass, fish, cheese.
2. Arm, foot, ribcage, spine
3. 1. child 2. baby 3. adult
4. Any sensible answer is OK.
5. Ham — growth, Fish — growth, Chocolate — energy, Spaghetti — energy.
6. Jellyfish — No skeleton
   Rabbit — Internal skeleton
   Beetle — External skeleton
7. Any sensible answers are OK. Here are some examples:
   Fatty Food — butter, cheese; Fish — sardines, salmon;
   Sugary Food — sugar, sweets; Meat — chicken, pork;
   Starchy Food — bread, potatoes;
   Fruit and Veg — leeks, carrots.
8. mixture, energy, vegetables, meat, beans.
9. A will get shorter, B will get longer, A will get harder.
10. 1. The skull is upside down.
    2. The hips are where the ribcage should be.
    3. The ribcage is where the hips should be.
    4. The ribcage is upside down.
    5. The arms/legs are where the legs/arms should be.
11. Bacon, sausage and eggs — Frank
    Spaghetti and meatballs — Angie
    Baked potato, beans and lentils — Susie
12. Slug, because it doesn't have a skeleton. The lobster has an external skeleton and the tortoise has an internal skeleton, so they can't bend as easily.

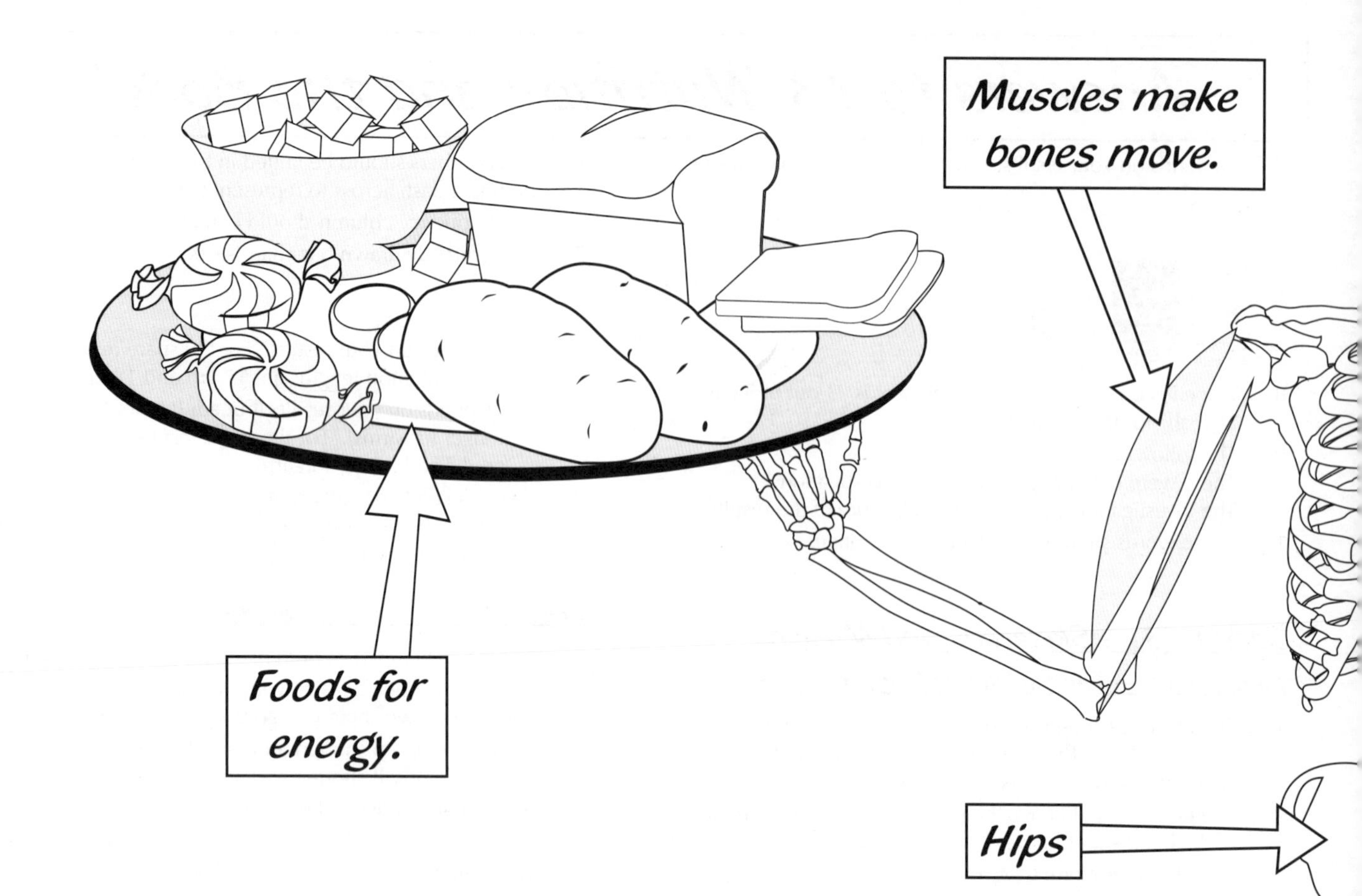

NUTRITION & THE BODY

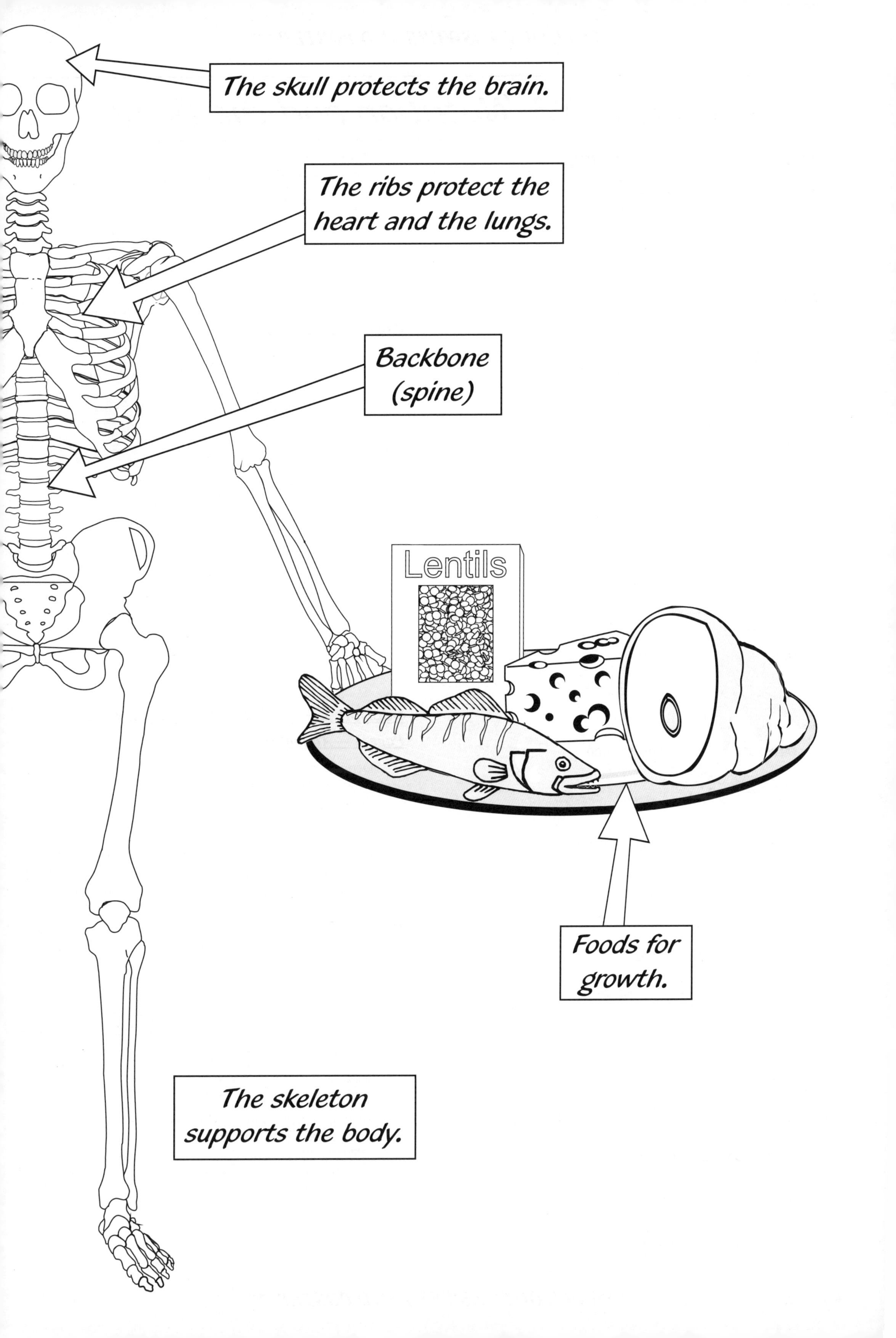
The skull protects the brain.
The ribs protect the heart and the lungs.
Backbone (spine)
Lentils
Foods for growth.
The skeleton supports the body.

Answers to Y3 'Nutrition and the Body'

Section 1 — Food for Humans

Page 1 — Animals Need Food

1. The apple, chips and egg should be ticked.
2. Any sensible answer is OK.
3. Any sensible answer is OK.

Pages 2-3 — Food Groups

1.

2.

Page 4 — Foods for Growth

1.

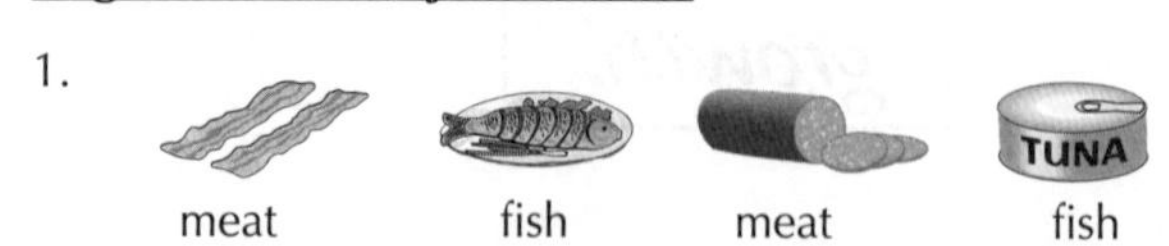

2. The left hand plate should be ticked.
3. Beans, lentils, meat (or beef/lamb/pork), fish and chicken (or turkey).
4. Eggs, and any kind of pulse, meat and fish are all OK.

Page 5 — Foods for Energy

1.

2. moving, exercise, more, more, weight
3. These two lists should be circled:

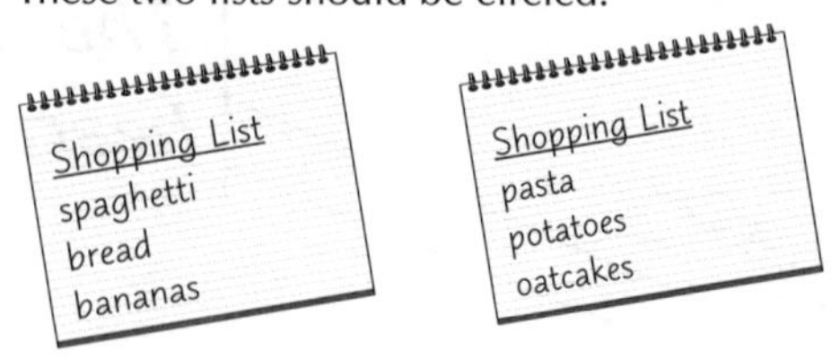

Page 6 — Balanced Diets

1. & 2.

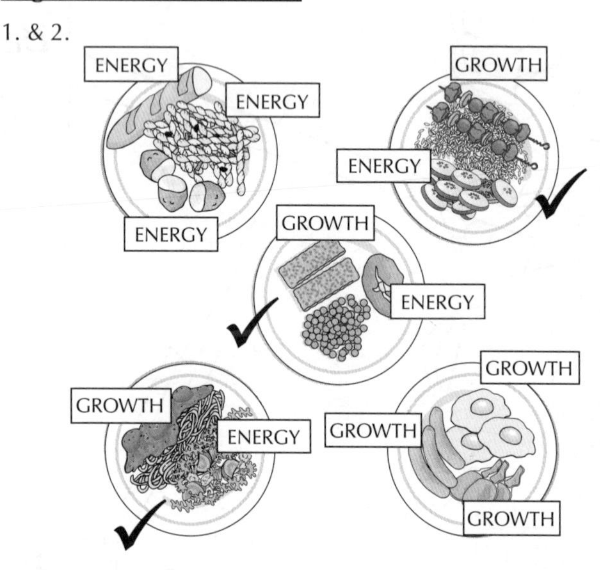

Section 2 — Food for Other Animals

Page 7 — Animal Diets

1. Depends on your research. These are example answers:
   Dogs eat: meat, tinned dog food, dry dog biscuits.
   Budgerigars eat: seeds, bark, buds.
   Goats eat: grass, hay, vegetables (e.g. cabbage, carrots).
   Snakes eat: mice, insects.
   Rabbits eat: seeds, grass, vegetables (e.g. lettuce, carrots).
2. Dogs and snakes should be circled. Budgerigars, goats and rabbits should have rectangles drawn around them.

Pages 8-10 — What Do Cats Eat?

1. "Do cats eat fish?" should be circled.
2. He should only use cats.
3. About 5 cats.
4. These words should be circled: only, fish, fish.
5. Depends on your results. This table uses the spare results.

	Tim	Emily	Dave	Neil	Ian
Day 1	✓	✓	✗	✗	✗
Day 2	✗	✗	✗	✓	✗
Day 3	✗	✓	✗	✗	✗

6. Depends on your results. This chart uses the spare results.

	Tally — number of cats	Total
EATS FISH	III	3
DOESN'T EAT FISH	II	2

PULL OUT ANSWERS AND POSTER

Animals with Skeletons

Loads of animals have skeletons inside them. They don't all look the same though. A dog skeleton looks different from a human skeleton — no surprises there.

1. Have a look at these skeletons. Write underneath each one what animal it's from.

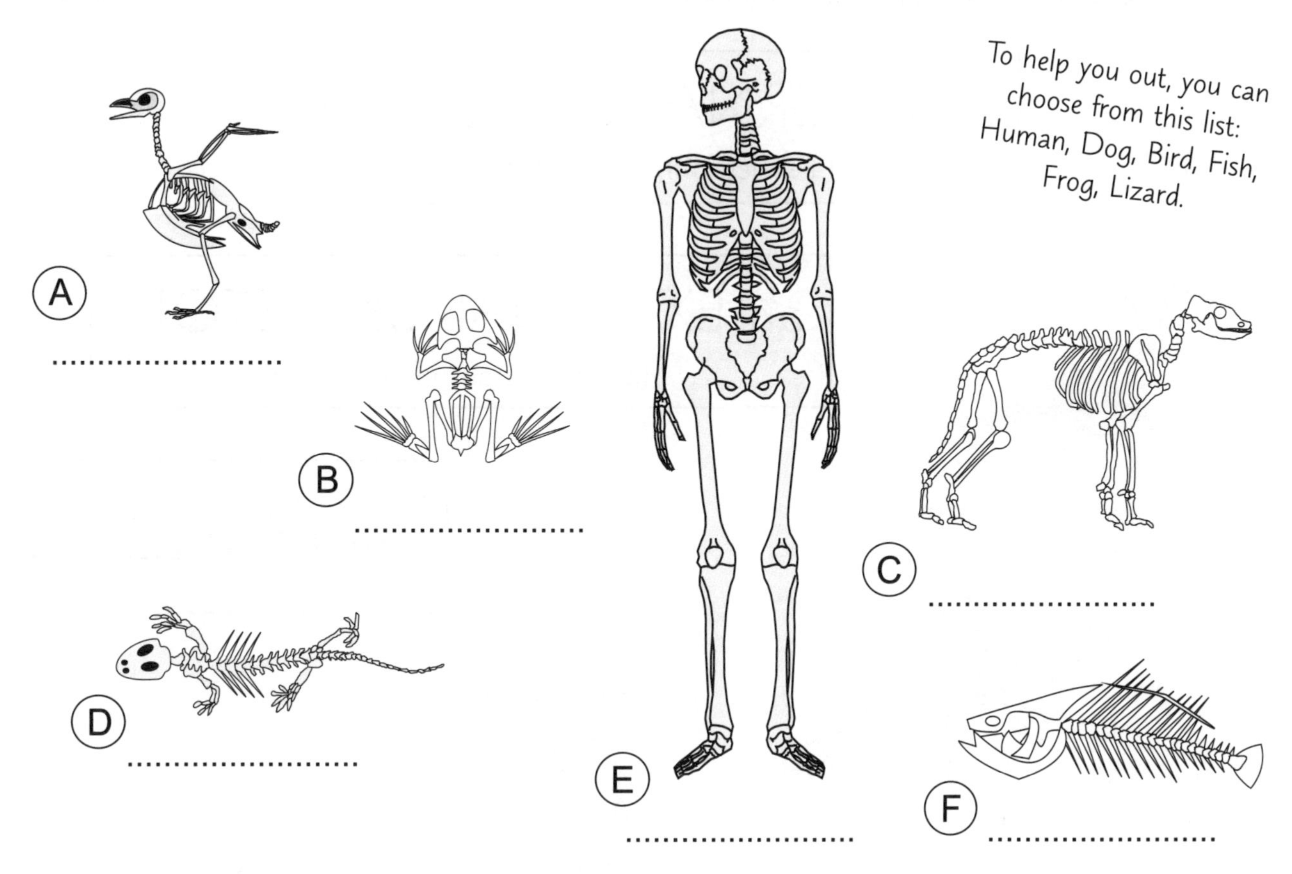

2. Look at the human and dog skeletons above and tick (✔) 'Yes' or 'No' for each question below.

Human	Yes	No
Does it have ribs?	☐	☐
Does it have a skull?	☐	☐
Does it have fingers?	☐	☐
Does it have a tail?	☐	☐
Does it have a spine?	☐	☐

Dog	Yes	No
Does it have ribs?	☐	☐
Does it have a skull?	☐	☐
Does it have fingers?	☐	☐
Does it have a tail?	☐	☐
Does it have a spine?	☐	☐

INVESTIGATE

We can work out what extinct animals might have looked like from their skeletons. Look up some dinosaur skeletons and draw what you think the dinosaurs looked like.

The Skeleton Supports the Body

Not all animals have skeletons <u>inside</u> their bodies. Some have skeletons <u>outside</u> their bodies — like a hard shell. And some <u>don't</u> have any skeleton at all — they're floppy or squidgy.

1. Write under each animal whether it has:

an INTERNAL SKELETON
(a skeleton <u>inside</u> its body)

an EXTERNAL SKELETON
(a skeleton <u>outside</u> its body)

NO SKELETON

....

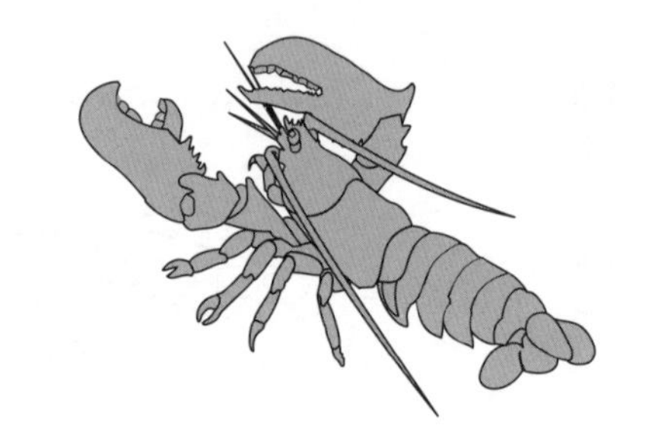

....

....

....

....

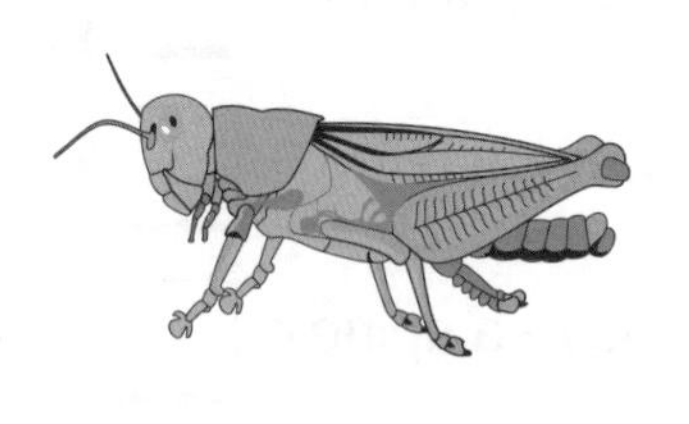

....

....

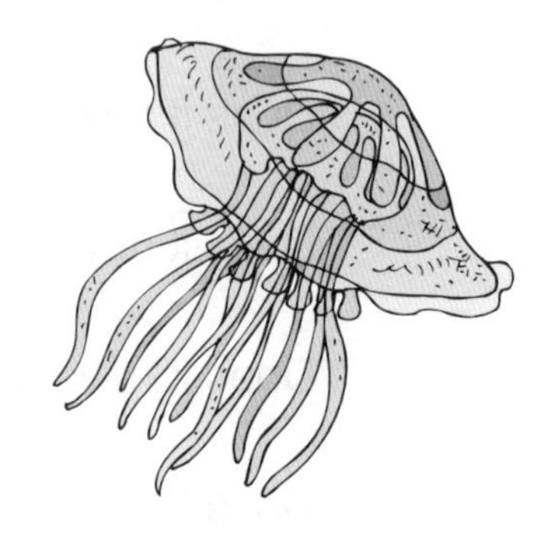

....

The Skeleton Supports the Body

2. These animals all have **internal** skeletons. (Circle) the places on their legs and arms (if they have them) where they can **bend**. Don't worry about the joints in their fingers and toes.

3. Here are some animals that either don't have skeletons or have external skeletons. (Circle) the ones you think can **bend all over**.

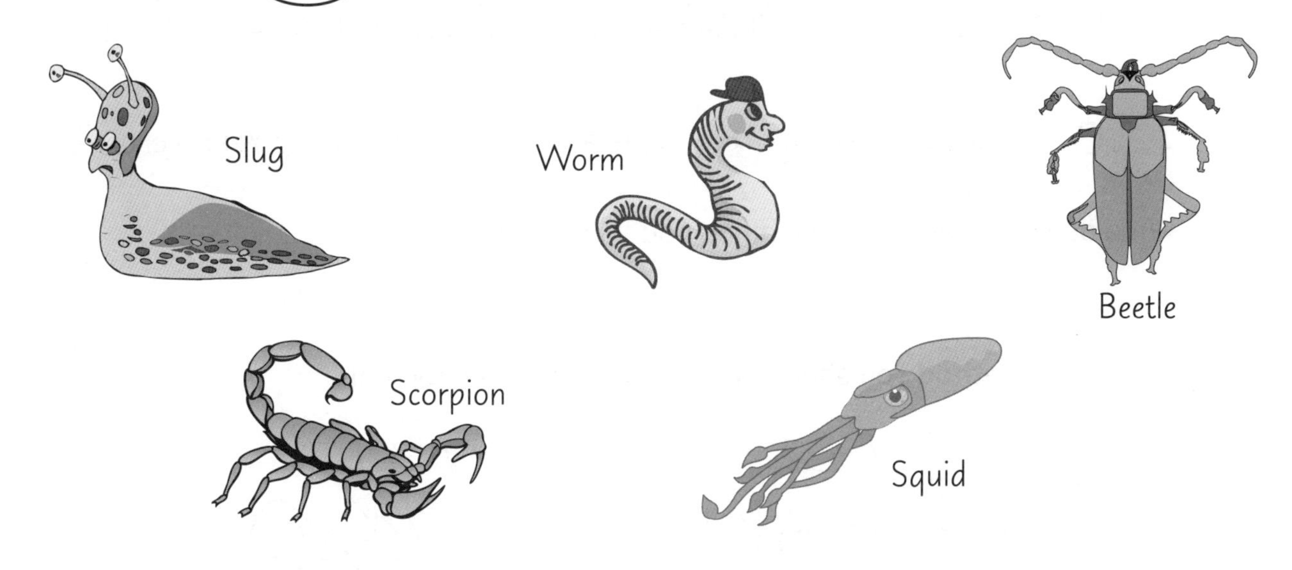

4. Do you think that having a skeleton makes an animal **more** or **less flexible**? Put a tick (✔) by the right answer.

Flexible is another word for bendy.

Animals with skeletons are more flexible. 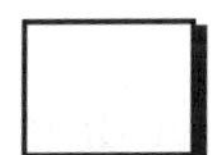

Animals with skeletons are less flexible. 

INVESTIGATE

Find some worms on your school field and watch how they move (this might be easier on a rainy day). How do you think humans would move if they didn't have a skeleton?

Comparing Bone Lengths

In this project, you'll be investigating whether Year 3 children or grown-ups have longer forearms.

1. You haven't done the experiment yet, so you can't know for sure what the answer will be. But you can make a guess. Tick (✔) the answer you think will be true.

Year 3 children and adults have the same length forearms. ☐

Year 3 children have longer forearms than adults. ☐

Year 3 children have shorter forearms than adults. ☐

2. Here are **three** different ways you could do the experiment.

A Measure the length of the forearms of 1 adult and someone from Year 3.

B Measure the length of the forearms of 20 adults and 20 Year 3 children.

C Measure the length of the whole arm of 20 adults and 20 Year 3 children.

Write down the letter of the method you think is **best**. ....

3. Here's the **method** you should use to get your measurements.

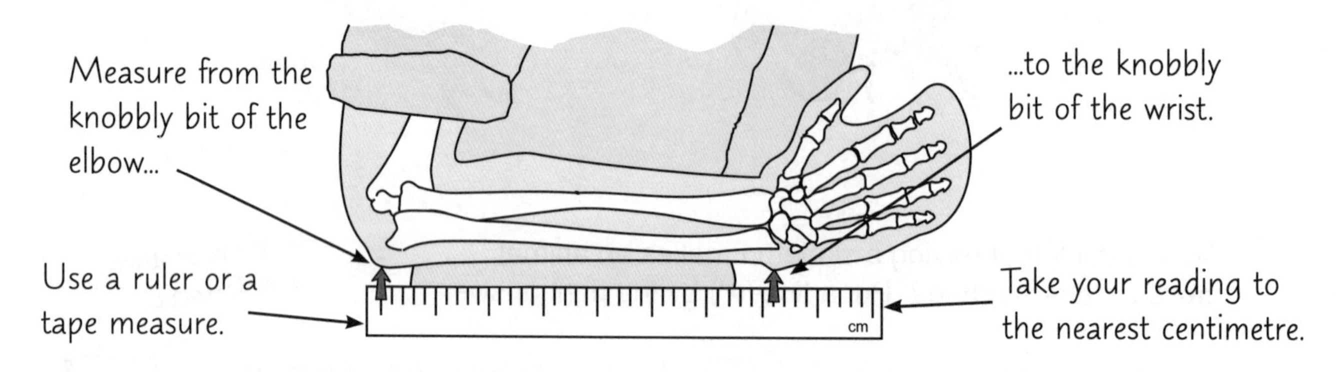

Circle the things below that would help make your investigation a fair test.

Measure to and from the same points on every arm.

Measure everyone's arm on a different day.

Use the same ruler or tape measure for every arm you measure.

Comparing Bone Lengths

4. Measure the forearms of 20 Year 3 pupils. Fill in the table below to show the lengths of their forearms.

Frequency means how many of something you have. Work it out by adding up the tally marks.

Use this space to write down each length after you measure it. I've done an example for you, so you only need to find 19 more.

Sean — 17 cm

Length of forearm to the nearest cm	Tally	Frequency
15		
16		
17	I	
18		
19		
20		
21		
22		
23		
24		

If you can't find 19 Year 3 pupils, then use some or all of the spare numbers at the bottom of the page.

5. Use the grid below to make a bar chart of your results.

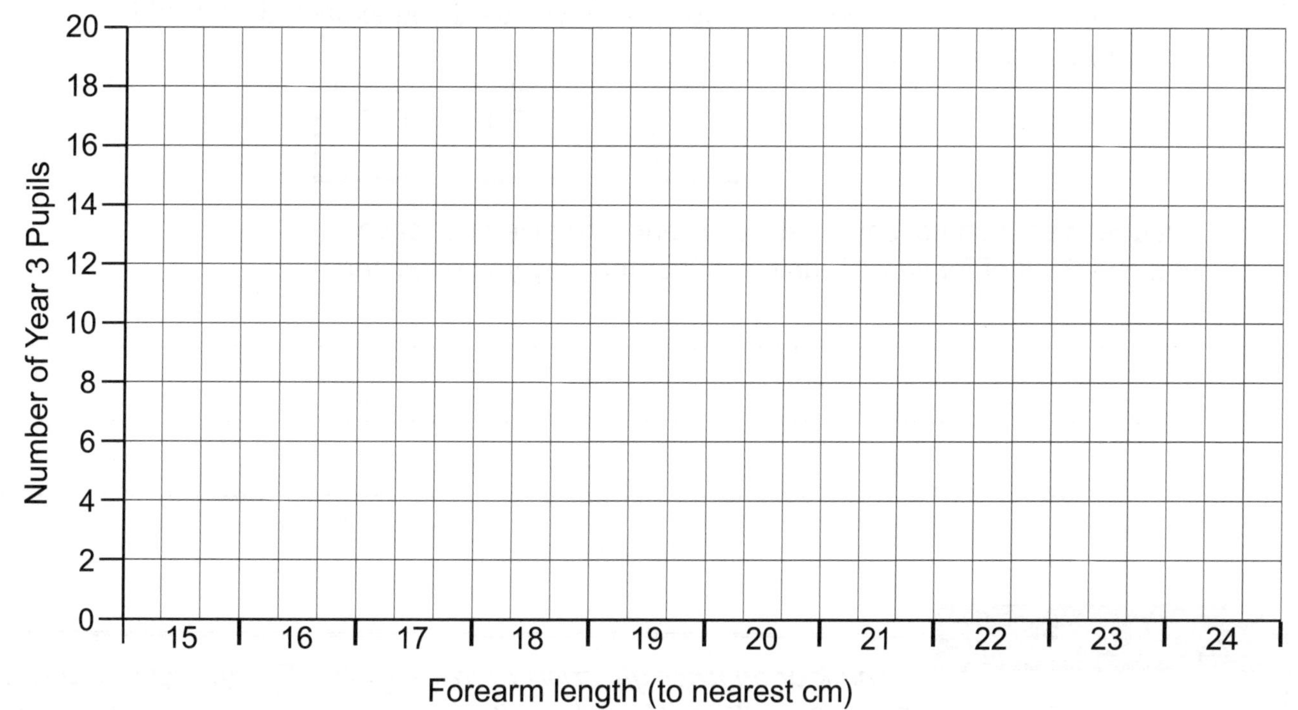

Spare Numbers: 18, 19, 20, 17, 18, 17, 17, 19, 15, 16, 18, 18, 19, 17, 20, 16, 18, 19, 16

Comparing Bone Lengths

6. This bar chart shows the forearm lengths of 20 **adults**.

How many adults had forearms that were **23 cm** long?

....

How many adults had forearms **more** than **25 cm** long?

....

HINT: You'll have to add some bars together to find the answer to the second part.

Number of adults
0
1
2
3
4
5
23
24
25
26
27
28
Length of forearm (to nearest cm)

7. Fill in the gaps in these sentences to show what the **results** of the experiment are.

1. The most common length of forearm for the adults is .... cm to the nearest cm.
2. The most common length of forearm for the Year 3 pupils is .... cm to the nearest cm.
3. The group of .... had the longest forearms.

If there are two lengths which are the most common, write them both down.

8. Does what you've found out match up to what you said you expected on p.16? Tick (✔) one box.

Yes ☐ No ☐ Sort of ☐

If it doesn't match up, say what's different, and give any reasons you can think of for why it didn't work out the way you expected.

....

....

....

EXTRA PROJECT

Think of another question to investigate. For example, you could compare the forearms of Year 3 pupils to Year 4 pupils. Or you could compare the length of a different body part. Make a plan, then do your new investigation.

Muscles and Bones

Humans and other animals have skeletons with muscles attached.
When muscles work they get shorter and pull on the bones — this makes the animal move.

1. Try bending your arms and legs. Feel which **muscles** are working.
   Colour in the arrows pointing to the right muscles.

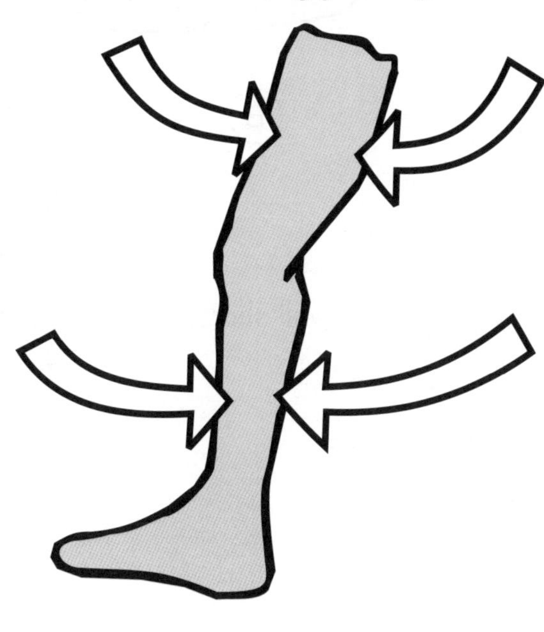

2. Bending your arm

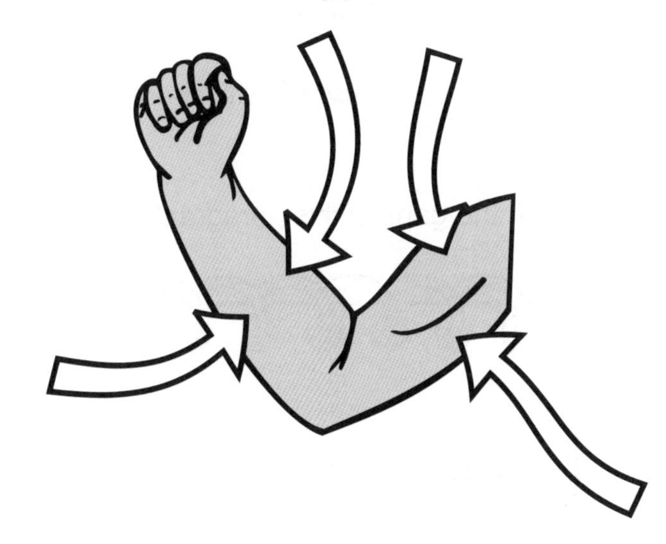

2. This picture shows muscles and bones in the **arm**. Draw an arrow from the end of each sentence to the part of the arm it's describing.

Shortens to make the arm bend.

Lengthens when the arm straightens.

Shortens to make the arm straight.

Lengthens when the arm bends.

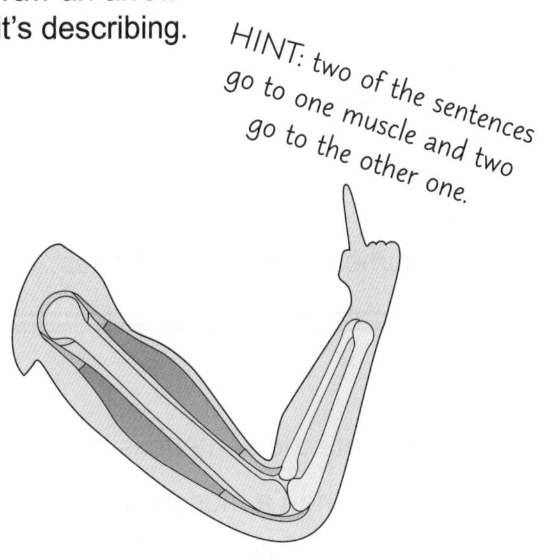

Muscles and Bones

3. A and B are a pair of muscles. When one muscle contracts and shortens, the other muscle relaxes and lengthens back to its original shape. Look at the diagram and use the words to complete the sentences.

   1. If the leg bends, ...

      and ....

   2. If the leg straightens, ...

      and ....

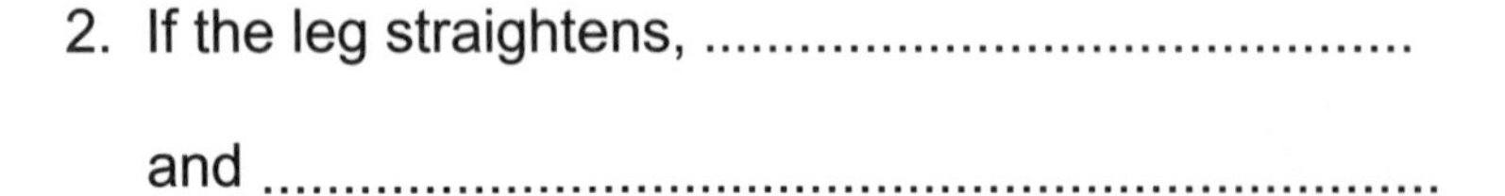

Muscle A will lengthen   Muscle B will lengthen

Muscle B will shorten   Muscle A will shorten

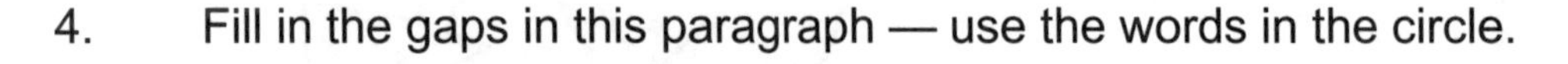

4. Fill in the gaps in this paragraph — use the words in the circle.

Muscles are attached to .... , and come in .... A muscle gets shorter to pull on the bones to .... them.
When one muscle in a pair contracts, the other muscle .... The relaxed muscle also .... because it gets pulled by some of the moving bones.

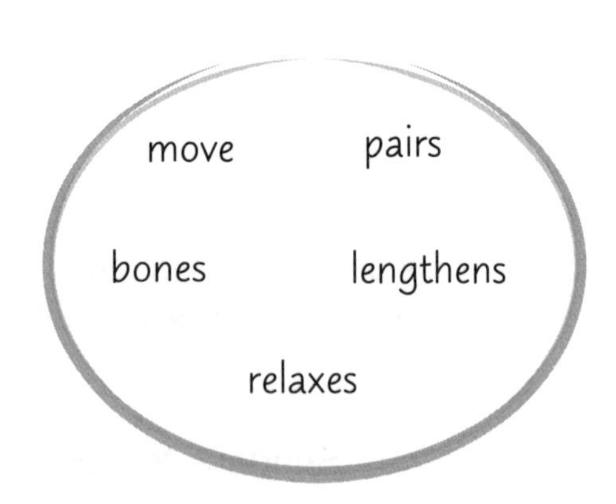

5. Complete the sentences by circling the right word in the brackets.

   When a muscle works, it (CONTRACTS / RELAXES).

   A muscle gets (SOFT / HARD) when it shortens.

   When one muscle in a pair contracts, the other (ALSO CONTRACTS / RELAXES).

Muscles and Bones

6. Tick (✔) the box pointing to the muscle that must **contract** to make this arm **straighten out**.

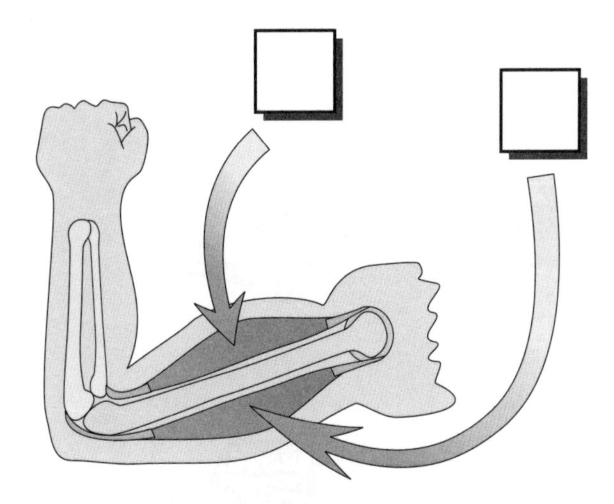

7. Look at that huge great arm up there. What will happen to it if the muscle on **top** contracts? Put a circle around the correct answer.

It will bend even more.

It will break.

It will straighten.

It will explode.

8. Tick (✔) the box pointing to the muscle that works the **most** when a leg **straightens**.

Back of Leg

Front of Leg

Would that muscle you have ticked get shorter, or longer?

....

HINT: Try feeling the muscles in your leg as you straighten it.

INVESTIGATE

Get a friend to hold their arm straight. Measure the distance around the middle of their upper arm using a tape measure. Then get them to bend their arm and measure it again. Write your measurements down. What do you notice? Why do you think this happened?

Mixed Questions

These four pages test everything you've learnt about nutrition and the body. They're all mixed up, but they should be no problem if you know your stuff.

1. Circle all the things that animals could get **nutrition** from.

2. Write the name of the set of bones under each picture.

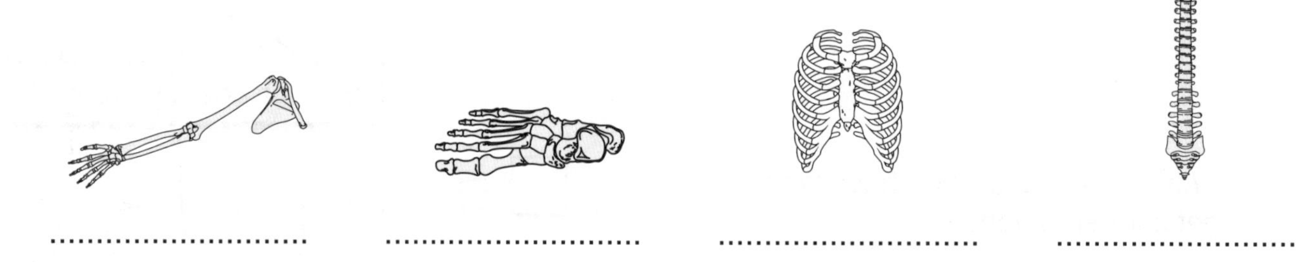

....

3. Write under each skeleton what stage of life the human was at. You can choose from **baby**, **child** and **adult**.

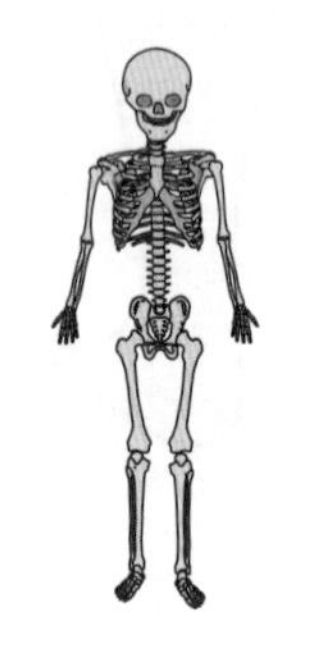

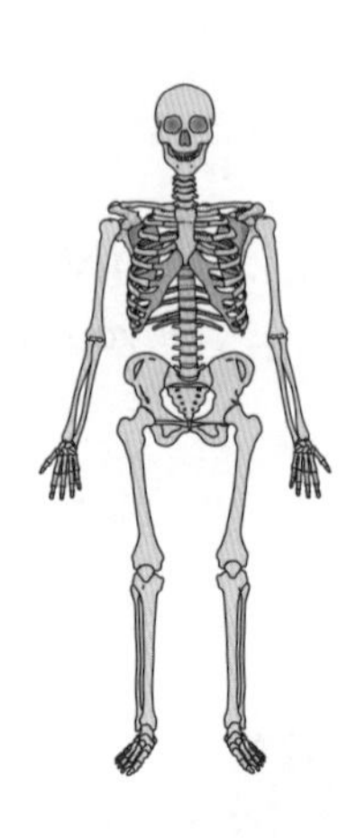

1. .... 2. .... 3. ....

Mixed Questions

4. Name **three** wild animals and write **one** thing they eat.

Name of wild animal	What it eats

5. Are these foods good for **growth** or **energy**? Write **growth** or **energy** under each one.

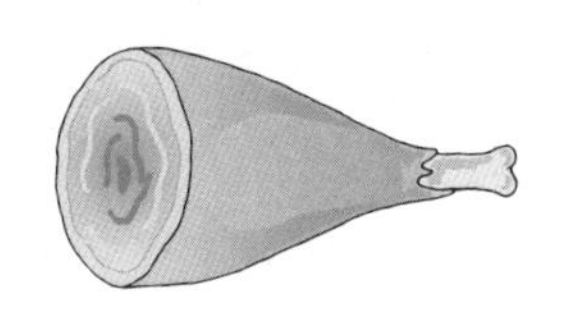

....

....

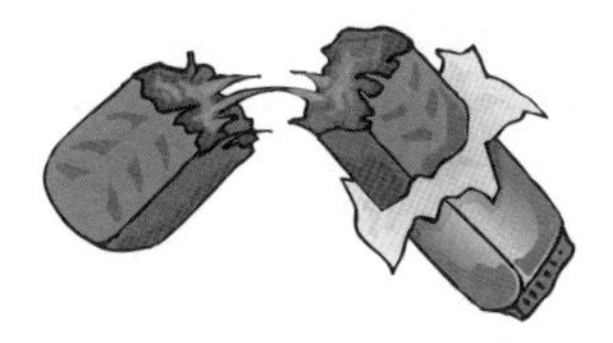

....

....

6. Write under each animal what type of skeleton it has — **internal**, **external** or **no skeleton**.

....

....

....

7. Name **two** foods for each of these food groups.

FATTY FOOD

1. ....
2. ....

FISH

1. ....
2. ....

SUGARY FOOD

1. ....
2. ....

MEAT

1. ....
2. ....

STARCHY FOOD

1. ....
2. ....

FRUIT AND VEG

1. ....
2. ....

Mixed Questions

8. Fill in the blanks in these sentences about a balanced diet. Use the words from the tin.

Eating a balanced diet means you have to eat the right .... of foods.

You have to eat the right amount of growth foods, ... foods and ....

Vegetarians don't eat .... so they need to eat growth foods like .... and lentils.

9. This leg is going to **bend** at the knee in the direction of the arrow. Answer these questions using **A** or **B**.

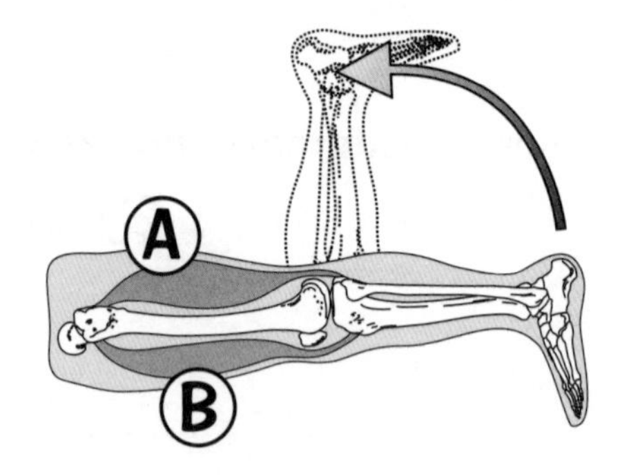

Which muscle will get shorter? ....

Which muscle will get longer? ....

Which muscle will get harder? ....

10. Fill in the gaps to describe the **six** mistakes in the drawing of the skeleton below. One has been done for you.

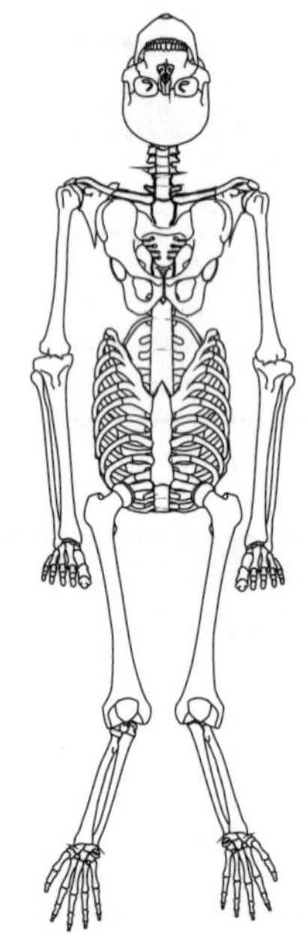

1. The skull is upside down.
2. The hips are where the .... should be.
3. The ribcage is where the .... should be.
4. The .... is upside down.
5. The .... are where the .... should be.

Mixed Questions

11. Rob has prepared a **different meal** for each of his **three** friends.
Read the information about his friends, and then write one of their names under each plate.

> Angie is playing a game of football after the meal.
> Susie is a vegetarian.
> Frank wants to grow big muscles.

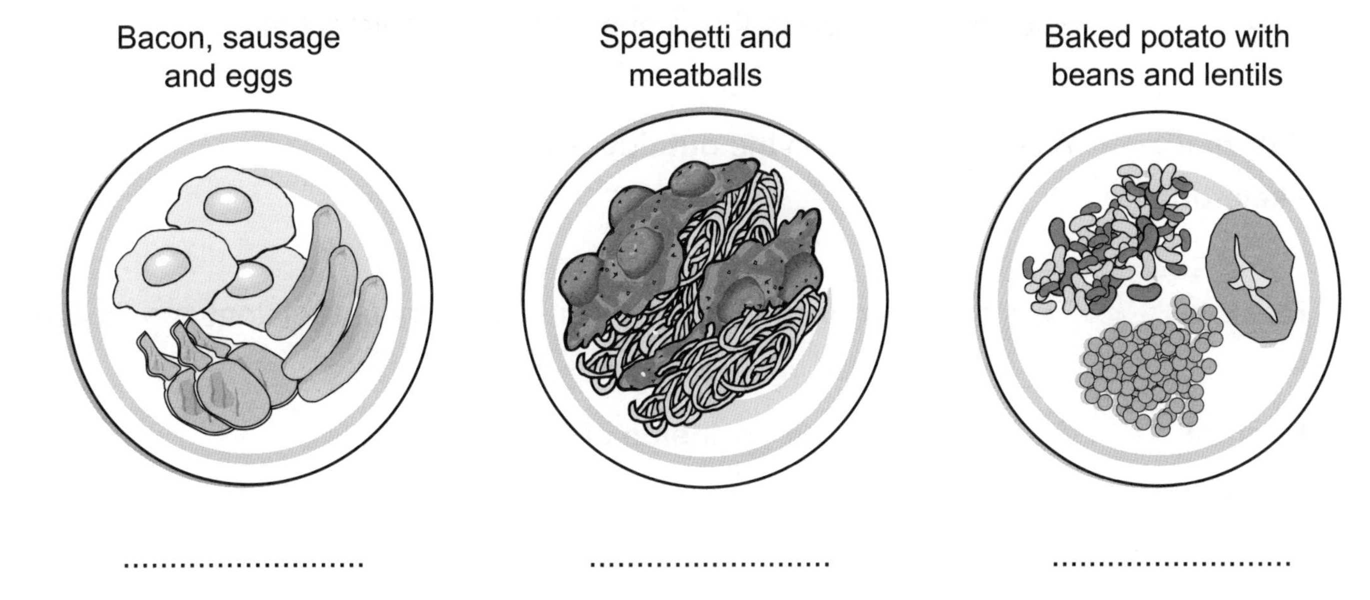

....

12. Which of the animals below is the most **flexible**? Explain your answer.

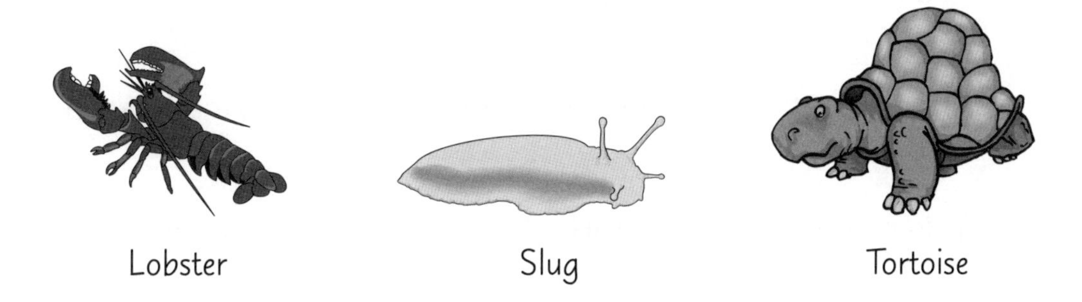

The most flexible animal is the ....

Reason: ....

....

....

Glossary

Balanced diet	This means eating a mixture of foods for **energy**, foods for **growth** and **vegetables**.
Contract	When muscles contract they get **shorter** and **harder**.
Diet	The mixture of **foods** that a human or other animal **eats**.
External skeleton	A skeleton that's on the **outside** of the body.
Flexible	This is another word for **bendy**. Animals without skeletons are flexible.
Internal skeleton	A skeleton that's on the **inside** of the body.
Muscle	These let the body **move** by **pulling** on bones. Muscles **contract** when they are doing work.
Nutrition	Eating the foods you need to stay **healthy**. You can do this by having a balanced diet.
Ribcage	The part of the skeleton that **protects** organs like the **heart** and **lungs**.
Skeleton	This **protects** and **supports** the body. It's made up of lots of **bones**.
Skull	The main **head** bone. It protects the brain.
Spine	The bone that joins the skull to the hips. It's also called the **backbone**.
Starchy	Contains **starch**. Pasta, bread and rice are examples of starchy foods. Starch gives the body **energy**.

S3B22